ZAAHIR & JAMEL THE CAMEL

HAJJ

by
Amatullah AlMarwani

G000022330

Goodwordkidz
Helping you build a family of faith

Zaahir & Jamel are friends fast and true,
Where one goes, the other goes, too.

With a brand-new adventure each and every day,
They invite you to join their fun along the way.

The time is here! There's a Hajj trip to make!
Let's watch and learn the steps they take …

2

"Come on Jamel, we have to plan and prepare,
When we get to Makkah, we'll be busy there!"

Zaahir & Jamel carefully think it all through,
Each item to take is precious, though few:

Clean clothes for Ihram, seamless and white,
The Holy Qur'an, to read day and night!

4

Zaahir & Jamel study the Pillar of Hajj long and hard,
They understand the Journey and what makes it Fard.

Allah Says in His Grand and Magnificent Book
(it's really in there, go take a look!):

"And Pilgrimmage to the House is a duty for Allah that you owe..."
Once in their life, with money and health, all Muslims must go.

Across the wide globe, from every nation and place,
Worshippers stream to Makkah at a steady pace.

Zaahir & Jamel join the Muslims coming on planes,
Others travel by foot, cars, boats and trains.

The excitement on their faces is plain and easy to see,
Everyone wants to earn life in Jennah for eternity!

Zaahir & Jamel perform
ghusl and get dressed,
Every good action would
now be truly blessed.

With the intention of Hajj and
Praise to Allah on their lips,
They wrap one cloth over their shoulder,
the other around their hips.

The words of Talbiyah fill them
with energy and verve.
Labayk Allahumma!
"Here we come and You we serve!"

11

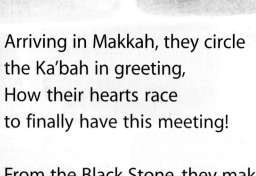

Arriving in Makkah, they circle
the Ka'bah in greeting,
How their hearts race
to finally have this meeting!

From the Black Stone, they make
Tawwaf seven times 'round,
Ending each turn with "Allahu Ahkbar!"
Oh, what a wonderful sound!

At the Station of Abraham,
mindful of others already there,
Zaahir & Jamel offer their own
two ra'kat prayer.

13

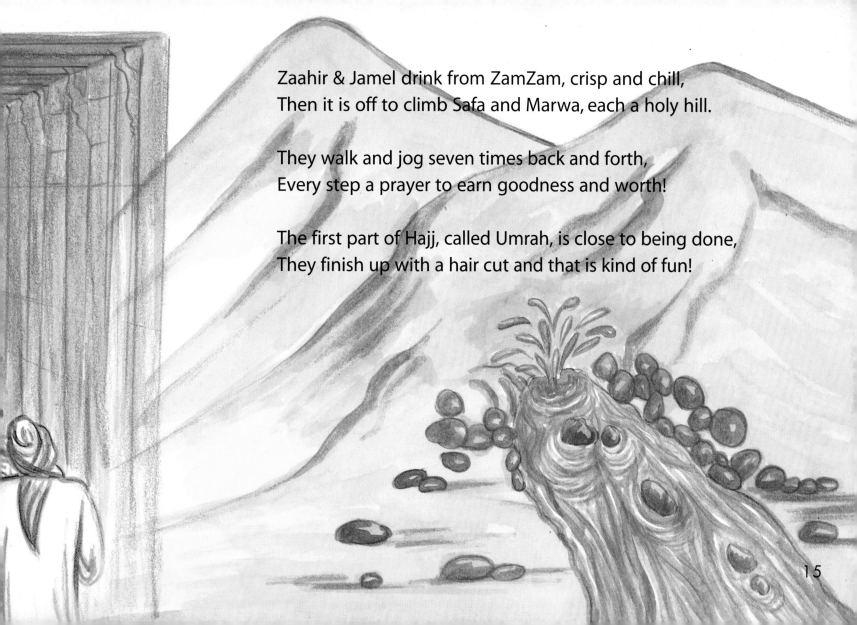

Zaahir & Jamel drink from ZamZam, crisp and chill,
Then it is off to climb Safa and Marwa, each a holy hill.

They walk and jog seven times back and forth,
Every step a prayer to earn goodness and worth!

The first part of Hajj, called Umrah, is close to being done,
They finish up with a hair cut and that is kind of fun!

To complete the Pilgrimage
and get it just right,
All the Muslims next go
to Mina for the night.

From Mina to Mount Arafat
a place of many benefits to reap,
Zaahir & Jamel make du'aa,
their concentration deep.

After Maghrib and Isha at Muzdalifah,
they finally seek out a rest,
Everyone proudly gives Allah
their spiritual and physical best.

Zaahir & Jamel, at Mina again
cast stones at the columns of the devil.
They praise Allah and curse shaytan
each time they throw a pebble.

A sacrifice is made and shared
by every single Pilgrim.
(Except for Jamel... he decides
a salad will better fill him)!

The rites are done, their heads are shaved,
it is time to say goodbye.
One more farewell to the Ka'bah,
Ya, Rabb! How the time did fly!

19

On their way home, Zaahir & Jamel talk fondly about the trip,
They want you to benefit, too, so here's their little tip:

Loving Islam gives us patience, pride and a feeling truly great,
Offering The Hajj like our Prophet is something we all await!

Obeying Allah and worshipping only Him will clean away our sins,
Every day we praise our Lord, a wonderful new blessing begins!

Games &

Learning about Islam is fun. Say "Bismillah" and jump right in!
You'll find all the answers on the last page (no peeking!)

Zaahir & Jamel's QUIZ:
1. The Hills which the Pilgrims run back and
    forth between are named:
    a. Jack & Jill
    b. Peanut Butter & Jelly
    c. Safa & Marwah
2. Where is the Ka'ba located?
3. What do pilgrims wear on the Hajj?
4. True or False: The Hajj is one of the eight
    pillars of Islam.
5. How do Muslims clean away their sins?
6. The drink of choice for the Muslims on the
    Hajj is:
    a. Kool-Aid
    b. Soda pop
    c. Zamzam water

Activities

Zaahir & Jamel's ARABIC ACTIVITY:

Zaahir and Jamel love to learn about the 99 Beautiful Names of Allah. One of His Names is "Al-Hameed" which means "The PraiseWorthy". The Qur'an says, *"Lo! He (Allah) is the Absolute. The Praiseworthy!"* (Surah 22: Ayah 64... Memorize this Name with Zaahir & Jamel!)

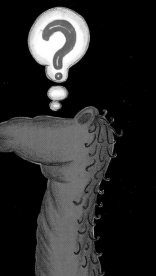

Practice writing Al-Hameed in Arabic (remember to start from the right and go to the left!):

الحميد

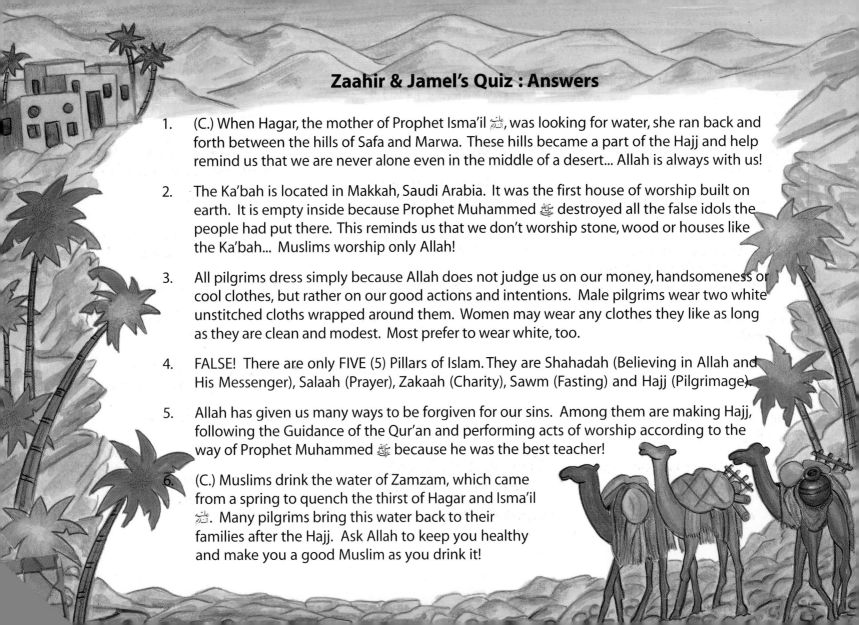

Zaahir & Jamel's Quiz : Answers

1. (C.) When Hagar, the mother of Prophet Isma'il عليه السلام, was looking for water, she ran back and forth between the hills of Safa and Marwa. These hills became a part of the Hajj and help remind us that we are never alone even in the middle of a desert... Allah is always with us!

2. The Ka'bah is located in Makkah, Saudi Arabia. It was the first house of worship built on earth. It is empty inside because Prophet Muhammed ﷺ destroyed all the false idols the people had put there. This reminds us that we don't worship stone, wood or houses like the Ka'bah... Muslims worship only Allah!

3. All pilgrims dress simply because Allah does not judge us on our money, handsomeness or cool clothes, but rather on our good actions and intentions. Male pilgrims wear two white unstitched cloths wrapped around them. Women may wear any clothes they like as long as they are clean and modest. Most prefer to wear white, too.

4. FALSE! There are only FIVE (5) Pillars of Islam. They are Shahadah (Believing in Allah and His Messenger), Salaah (Prayer), Zakaah (Charity), Sawm (Fasting) and Hajj (Pilgrimage).

5. Allah has given us many ways to be forgiven for our sins. Among them are making Hajj, following the Guidance of the Qur'an and performing acts of worship according to the way of Prophet Muhammed ﷺ because he was the best teacher!

6. (C.) Muslims drink the water of Zamzam, which came from a spring to quench the thirst of Hagar and Isma'il عليه السلام. Many pilgrims bring this water back to their families after the Hajj. Ask Allah to keep you healthy and make you a good Muslim as you drink it!